ON PARADE

SENIOR AUTHOR

Leo Fay

AUTHORS

Barbara D. Stoodt
Dorothy Grant Hennings
Joan M. Baker
Myron L. Coulter

Bilingual Materials
   George A. González

The Riverside Publishing Company

Acknowledgments: We wish to thank the following publishers, authors, photographers, illustrators and agents for permission to use and adapt copyrighted materials.

Illustration: YVETTE BANEK 33, 41–46   ALAIN GAUTIER 29–42   MICHELE GUIRE VAKA 6–10, 59–64   BRIAN KARAS 53–58   BEN MAHAN 5   BARBARA McCLINTOCK 47–52   LUCINDA McQUEEN 43–40   DIANE PATTERSON 11–16 FREYA TANZ 23–28

Cover Art: Tom Powers / Mulvey Associates

CONTENTS

How to Learn New Words

1. Look at the letters in the word.

2. Think of the sound clues.

3. Use the sentence clues.

4. Read the word.

How to Read for Meaning

1. Set a purpose.

2. Read the story.

3. Answer the question.

Super Pets

What a Jump!

Fred can jump.
Fred can jump to the .

6

Stanley wants to jump to the  .
Fred wants Stanley to jump to it.

Stanley can not.

7

Stanley can jump to a .
And Stanley can jump to a .
Can Stanley jump to the ?
Stanley can not.

8

Stanley can not jump to the  .
Stanley can jump to Fred.

And Fred and Stanley can jump
to the 🌙 .

10

LEARN NEW WORDS

1. The **hat** is out.
2. The **man** wants the hat.
3. Can the man **get** the hat?
4. The hat is not **on** the man.

11

Get the Hat

The man wants to get the hat.

It is on Rusty.

Can the man get the hat?

12

Now the hat is on the man.

Rusty wants the hat.

Can Rusty get it?

Rusty can.

13

Now the hat is on Rusty!
The man wants the hat.
The man can get on Rusty.
And the man can get the hat.

Now the hat is on the man.

And now it is on Rusty.

Rusty wants the hat.
And the man wants the hat.

15

Now Kate wants the hat.
Kate can jump.
Kate can get the hat.

Now the hat is not on Rusty.
And the hat is not on the man.
The hat is <u>in</u> Kate!

16

LEARN NEW WORDS

1. **Tell** what is in the .
2. It is a **pet**!
3. Is it **big**?

17

What Is It?

Find the pet.
Tell what it is.
Can the pet get on ?
It can!

18

Find the .
Is it big?
Tell what pet can jump
in the .

Can a pet get in a hat?
Find the big hat.
Tell what pet is in it.

Find the  .

It is not big.

Find the pet.

It is big.

Tell what it is.

Can the pet get in the  ?

Mrs. Berk wants to get
to the  .
Can Gus get Mrs. Berk to the ?
Find Gus.
Gus is not a pet.
Tell what Gus is.

1. The **hill** is big.
2. **But** the boy is not.
3. The boy wants to go
   up the hill.
4. Can the boy get the **sack**
   up the hill?

Up the Hill

Find the sack.

Tom wants to get it up the hill.

But the sack is big.

Tom can not get it
up the hill.

But Tom can get Clover.

24

Can Tom get the sack on Clover?
Tom can not.
The sack is big.
And Tom is not.

Tom can not get the sack
up the hill.
And Clover can not.
But Tom can get Ben.
Can Ben get the sack up the hill?
Ben can not.

26

Now Clover and Ben find out
what is in the sack.
It is  .
Clover wants the  .
And Ben wants it.

Now the sack is not big.

Tom can get it on Ben.

And Ben can go up the hill.

28

Amy Wants a Pet

What is in the hat?
Matt can find a .
Peggy can find a .
But what can Amy find?

Amy wants a pet.

But Amy can not find a pet.

And Lee can not find a pet.

What can Lee find?

Lee can find a hill!

30

Amy and Lee go up the hill.

Amy and Lee find a ▢ .

What is in it?

31

It is not a .
It is not a hill.
It is a pet!
And what a pet it is!

32

ZOOM

Look

Think

Use

Read

◆ LEARN NEW WORDS

1. A **pig** is on the hill.
2. A **pot** is on the hill.
3. **Did** the pig find the pot?
4. The pig can **hide** in the pot.
5. Did the pig go **down** the hill?

34

Hide!

Max wants to hide.

Tess wants to hide.

Max and Tess find a pot.

Max can hide in the pot.

Tess can hide in the pot.

35

The pig can find the pot.
Can the pig find Max?
Can the pig find Tess?
The pig can not.

Now the pig is on the hill.
Did Max hide on the hill?
Did Tess hide on the hill?
Max and Tess did not.

The pig did not find Max.

The pig did not find Tess.

But the pig did find Henry.

Now Henry wants to get the pig.

Go, pig, go.

Go down the hill and hide.

38

The pig is down the hill.
And Henry is down the hill.
The pig wants to hide.
The pig wants to hide in the pot.

Now the pig is in the pot.
And Max and Tess get out.

The pig did not find Max.
The pig did not find Tess.
But what did Henry find?

LEARN NEW WORDS

1. The **bus** is on the hill.
2. The girls **run** up the hill.
3. The man **has** a hat.
4. The man can **see** the girls.

41

Run, Lucy!

Lucy has to get to the bus.

It can get Lucy to the airplane.

Lucy can see the bus.

But Mr. Benson can not see Lucy.

Lucy has to run.

Run, Lucy!

Lucy did not get to the bus.
Now the bus is on a hill.
Run, Lucy!
Run to the bus.

Pal and Red run up to Lucy.
Lucy has to tell Pal and Red
to get down.
Lucy can see the bus.
Lucy wants to get to it.
But Lucy can not.

Lucy has to run and run.
Now the bus is down the hill.
Run, Lucy!
Run down the hill.
Lucy can see the bus.
But Lucy can not get to it.

45

Now Mr. Benson can see Lucy.

But Lucy can see the airplane.

Lucy did not get to the bus.

But Lucy did get to the airplane!

46

LEARN NEW WORDS

1. The boy **will** go down the hill.
2. Will the boy **win**?
3. The boy can go **fast**.
4. What can go **as** fast **as** the boy?

47

The Big Jump

David is in a sack.

Pat is in a sack.

David and Pat will jump down
to the merry-go-round.

Will David win?

Will Pat win?

1, 2, 3, go!
Pat can jump fast.
David can not jump
as fast as Pat.
Will Pat win?

49

David wants to win.
David will jump fast.
David has to jump
as fast as Pat.

Now see David jump up.
Is David in a sack?

50

Now see David.
David is in the sack Pat is in!

David and Pat jump
to the merry-go-round.
Did David win?
Did Pat win?

52

1. The **rabbit** can run fast.
2. The **cats** can run fast.
3. Can **my** cats run as fast as the rabbit?
4. **No**, my cats can not.

Down the Hill Fast

My rabbit is fast.

It can go down hills fast.

See it go!

54

The rabbit is fast.
But no rabbit is as fast
as my cats.
My cats will win.

No, no!
My rabbit will win.

55

 See my pet.
It is a fast, fast turtle.
My turtle will win.

 No turtle can go fast.

 No turtle can go as fast
as my cats.

My turtle can go as fast
as the cats.
See it go.
It got down as fast
as the rabbit.
And it can go down as fast
as the cats.

 Now what pet can go
up the hill fast?
Can the rabbit?
Can the cats?

 No! No!

My turtle can go
 up hills fast.
Get on and see.

58

See the Hat Go!

Amos has a hat.

Is the hat on Amos?

It is not.

See the hat go!

Amos wants the hat.

Can Amos get it?

Now see the hat.

It is on the merry-go-round.

Can the cats get the hat?

The cats get on the merry-go-round.

But the cats can not get the hat.

Now the hat is on the airplane.

Can the rabbit get the hat?

No, the rabbit can not.

See the hat now.

It is up the hill.

The cats go up the hill.

Amos and the rabbit go up.

But now the hat is down.

The cats can not run now.

The rabbit can not run.

And Amos can not run.

But see the hat!

Amos did not get to the hat.

But the hat did get to Amos.